# 1. Using electricity safely

## Spot the hazard

The Wise family in this picture are using electricity safely.

Ask your teacher for a Spot the hazard copymaster.

The Barmy family in the copymaster picture are using electricity dangerously.

**Q1** On the copymaster circle 10 electrical dangers or hazards.

**Q2** Write down some rules about electrical safety that the Barmy family need to know.

**Q3** Draw a poster for the children of the Barmy family. Tell them how dangerous electricity is. Explain to them how to use electricity safely.

# 2. Electric circuits

**Apparatus**

- wires ■ bulb ■ motor ■ buzzer
- electrical symbols copymaster
- 1 battery

## Making a circuit

Electric circuits do useful jobs. They are made up of **components** such as bulbs, switches, batteries, bells and motors, connected together by wires. The picture shows you how to connect a battery (cell) to a bulb to make it light up. The bulb will only light if the circuit is a complete loop.

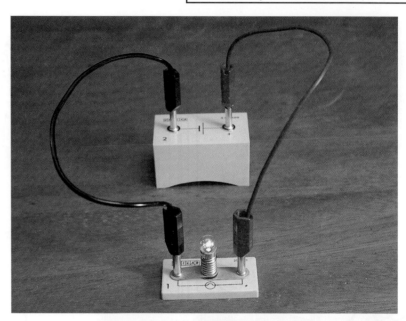

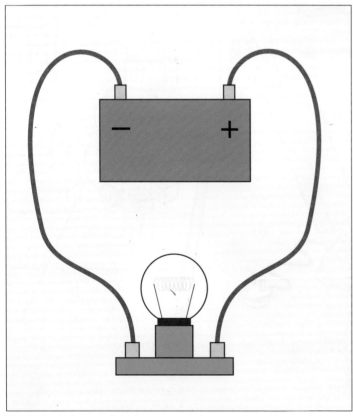

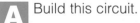 Build this circuit.

**B** Sarah is drawing a diagram of the circuit that she built. Use the Electrical symbols copymaster to help you draw a diagram of your circuit. Match each component in the circuit to its symbol.

**C** Repeat **A** and **B** for the buzzer and motor.

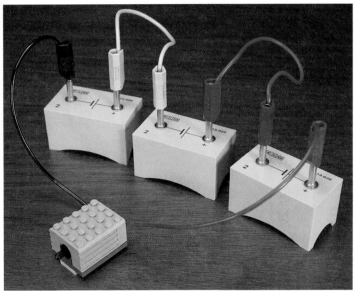

**Q1** Copy the boxes below. Match the component with what it did.

| | |
|---|---|
| motor | made a sound |
| bulb | turned |
| buzzer | gave out light |

**Q2** Draw the circuit diagram of this picture.

**Extension exercise 1 can be used now.**

## 2. Electric circuits

## Making a switch and sending a message

A switch is a component which is used to turn things on and off. When the switch is closed the circuit is on. When the switch is open the circuit is off. Let's make a switch and use it in a circuit.

**Apparatus**
- 2 drawing pins
- crocodile clips ■ wires ■ bulb
- paper clip
- Electrical symbol copymaster
- Morse code copymaster
- 1 battery

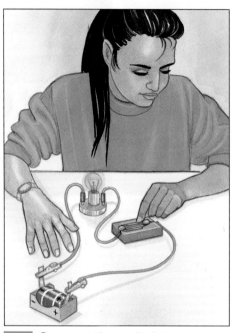

**A** Build this switch.

**B** Connect the switch to a battery and a bulb to make a circuit. Close the switch to make the bulb light up.

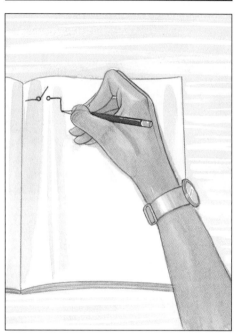

**C** Use the Electric symbol copymaster to find the symbol for a switch. Draw a circuit diagram of your circuit in your book.

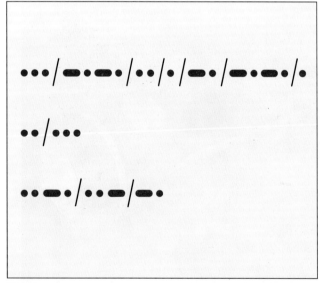

**D** Ask your teacher for the Morse code copymaster. Use your circuit to send this message to your friend.

**E** Make up your own message and send it to your friend.

# Using switches

Your teacher will discuss some important uses of switches.

**Q1** Copy this table.

| Device | Type of switch | Why this type of switch is used |
|--------|----------------|----------------------------------|
| door bell | push switch | the door bell only rings when the switch is pushed |

Look at the pictures below. Each device is controlled by a switch.

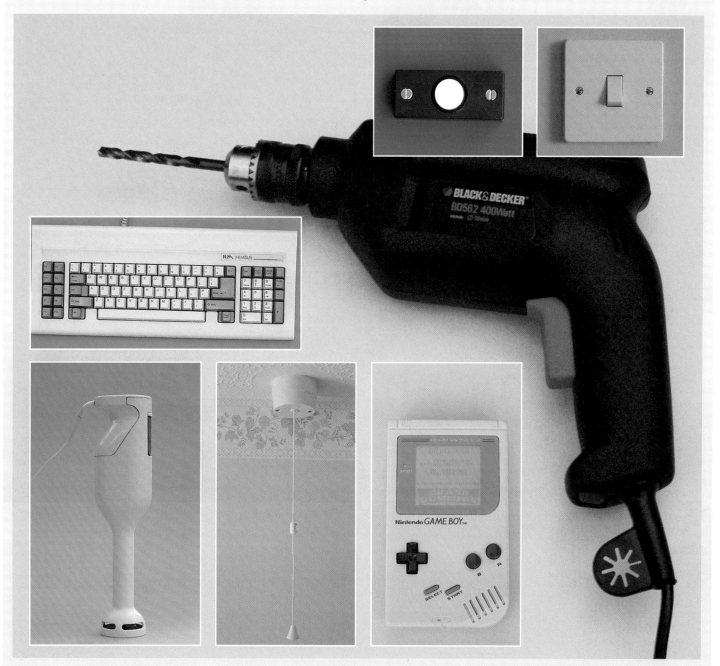

**Q2** Complete the table.

# Series circuits

In this activity you are going to build series circuits using a power pack. Power packs make mains electricity safer. A series circuit has the components joined together in one loop. These pupils are standing in series.

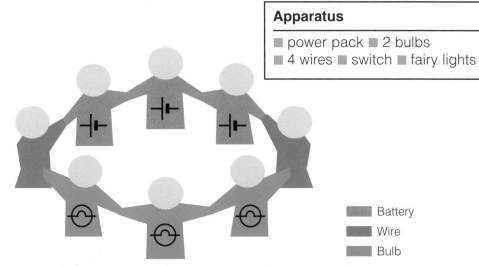

| | Apparatus |
|---|---|
| | ■ power pack ■ 2 bulbs |
| | ■ 4 wires ■ switch ■ fairy lights |

■ Battery
■ Wire
■ Bulb

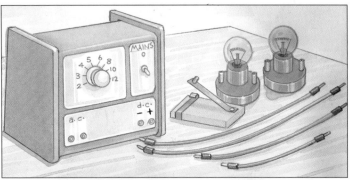

**A** Build a series circuit with two bulbs, wires and power pack. Draw a symbol diagram of your circuit in your book.

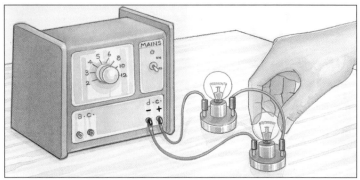

**B** Unscrew one of the bulbs. Notice what happens to the other bulb. Replace the bulb.

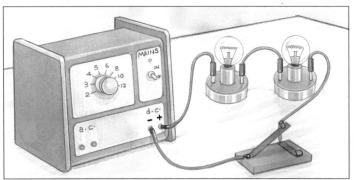

**C** Add the switch to your circuit. (To do this you will need to add another wire.) Open and close the switch. Answer **Q1** now.

**D** Fairy lights are connected in series. Your teacher will show you some fairy lights.

**Q1** Copy the table to show what happened to the bulbs in **C**.

| Switch | Bulbs |
|---|---|
| on off | |

**Q2** What will happen to the fairy lights if one bulb is removed?

**Q3** The lights in your house are not connected in series. Explain why not.

**Q4** Why would it be dangerous if the lights on a car were connected in series?

# Making a quiz card

Work in pairs. In this activity you are going to use a series circuit to make a quiz card. Series circuits only work when they are complete.

**Apparatus**

- Quiz card copymaster
- strips of aluminium foil
- scissors ■ sticky tape ■ wires
- buzzer ■ 2 batteries

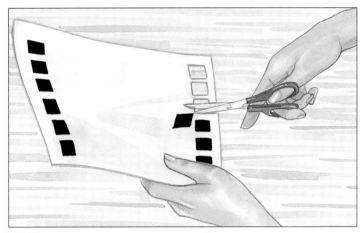

**A** Ask your teacher for the Quiz card copymaster. Cut out the black squares.

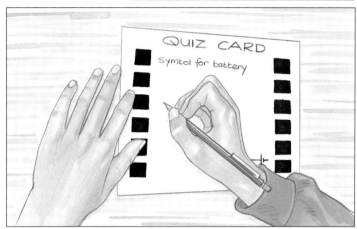

**B** Write down six questions about electricity and their answers. Do not put the right answer next to the question.

**C** Draw lines on the back of the card to match your questions to their correct answers. Show this to your teacher before you do **D**.

**D** Place a strip of aluminium foil on the line connecting your first question with its correct answer. Make sure the tin foil shows through the holes. Cover it completely with sticky tape. Do this for all the other questions. Glue a sheet of card to the back of your quiz card.

**Q1** Swap your card with another group. Use the buzzer to see if you answer the questions correctly. Do this at least five times.

**Q2** Draw the circuit diagram for question 1 of the quiz card in your book.

**Q3** Explain how your card works.

**E** Make a circuit with the buzzer, batteries, wires and your game card. The buzzer must sound when the answer is correct.

## 2. Electric circuits

## Parallel circuits

In this activity you are going to identify, build and draw parallel circuits. The picture shows pupils standing in parallel.

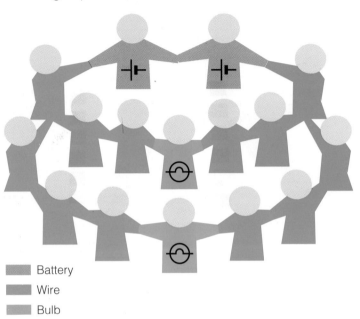

■ Battery
■ Wire
■ Bulb

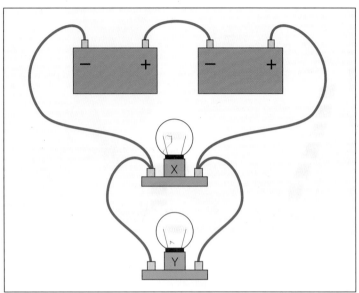

**A** Build this circuit and draw a diagram of it in your book using electric symbols.

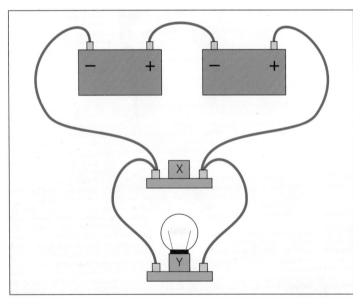

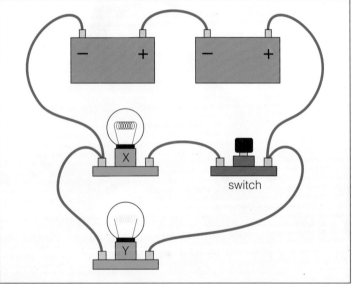

switch

**B** Remove bulb X. Notice what happens to bulb Y. Replace bulb X and remove bulb Y. Notice what happens to bulb X. Draw two diagrams in your book to show what happens in each case.

**D** Now build a circuit to switch bulb Y on and off. Draw the diagram in your book.

**E** Put the switch in the circuit so that it switches both bulbs on and off. Draw a diagram of your circuit in your book.

**C** Put a switch in your circuit to switch bulb X on and off. Draw the diagram in your book.

**Q1** What did you notice about the brightness of the bulbs in parallel compared to the same bulbs in series?

**Q2** What happened to bulb Y when you removed bulb X?

**Q3** How would this differ if the bulbs were in series?

# Parallel circuits in everyday life

**Q1** Look at the picture. Make a list of all the things you can see which use parallel circuits to make them work.

**Q2** Explain why parallel circuits are useful.

**Q3** Look at the diagram.

a Describe the circuit in your own words.
b Build the circuit.
c Remove bulb X. Explain what happens.
d Remove bulb Z. Explain what happens.

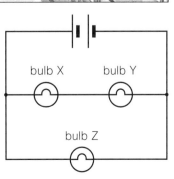

**Extension exercise 2 can be used now.**

# 3. Electric current

## Current in a circuit

When a battery is connected to a bulb electric charge flows around the circuit. The bulb lights up. We call this flow of charge an **electric current**. The units we measure it in are called **ampères** (**amps** or **A**). The size of the current is the same all the way around the circuit. The current going into the bulb is the same as the current coming out of the bulb. The current goes from the battery to the bulb and back to the battery. We measure the amount of current using instruments called ammeters.

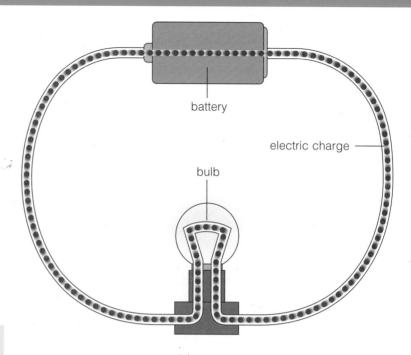

battery

electric charge

bulb

**Q1** Copy this table.

| Reading on first ammeter | Reading on second ammeter |
|---|---|
|  |  |

**Apparatus**

■ bulb ■ 2 digital ammeters ■ wires

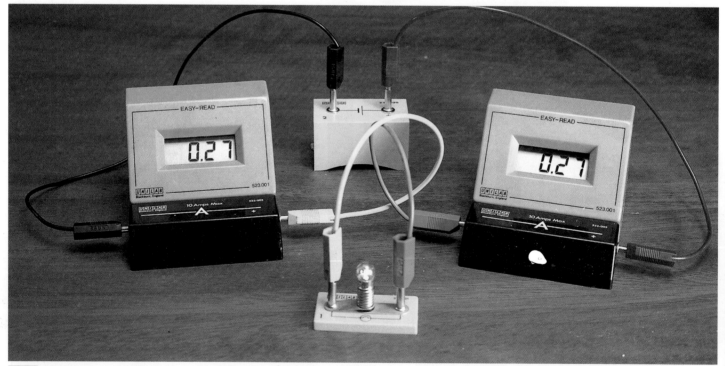

**A** Build this circuit and record the readings in the table.

**Q2** What do we call the flow of electric charge around a circuit?

**Q3** What units do we use to measure the flow of charge?

**Q4** Look at the picture. How can you tell that the bulb is not using up the current?

## The current puzzle

In this activity you are going to use your knowledge of current to make a display.

**A** Work in groups of four. Using a battery, a bulb and some wires, make a circuit. Stick your circuit on to a large sheet of card with sticky tape.

**Apparatus**

- 2 wires ■ bulb in holder
- battery in holder ■ sticky tape
- crayons or felt-tipped pens
- large sheet of card or stiff paper
- sticky white labels

**B** Discuss what is happening in each part of the circuit.

**C** To make labels for your circuit choose the correct words and sentences from the boxes. You can use each one as many times as you need.

bulb

wire

battery

There is an electric current in this wire.

There is no electric current in this wire.

There is a lot of electric current in this wire.

There is less electric current in this wire.

There is the same amount of electric current in this wire.

The current is used up as heat and light in the bulb.

The current is not used up in the bulb.

The current goes from the battery to the bulb.

The current goes from the bulb to the battery.

The current goes from the battery to the bulb in both wires.

# Measuring current

In this activity let's measure electric current. Current is measured in ampères using an **ammeter**. The current flowing through a large torch bulb is about 0.5 amps and through a car headlamp it is 3–4 amps.

Two types of ammeter are shown in the pictures.
One is **analogue** and the other is **digital**.

| Apparatus |
| --- |
| ■ bulb ■ motor ■ 3 batteries |
| ■ switch ■ ammeter ■ wires |

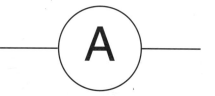

Ammeter symbol

▲ Analogue ammeter

Notice that both ammeters have **+** and **– terminals** (connecting points). The + terminal must lead to the + terminal of the battery, otherwise the pointer on the analogue ammeter will move in the wrong direction. The digital ammeter would give a negative reading.

It is very easy for electric current to flow through an ammeter. Too much current will damage it. You must never connect an ammeter directly across a battery.

| Safety note: Check with your teacher before you switch on. |
| --- |

▲ Digital ammeter

**Q1** Copy this table.

| Number of batteries | Brightness of bulb | Ammeter reading |
|---|---|---|
| 1 | | |
| 2 | | |

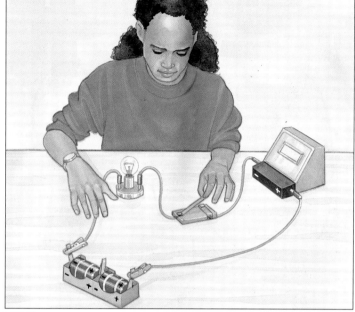

**A** Fiona is investigating the effect of adding more batteries on the electric current. Build her circuit. Close the switch. Read the ammeter. Complete the

**B** Add another battery to the circuit. Close the switch. Read the ammeter. Complete the table in **Q1**. Repeat **B** once more.

**C** Add another bulb to the circuit. Close the switch. Read the ammeter.

**D** Replace the bulbs with a buzzer. Repeat **A** and **B**. Complete the table in **Q2**.

**Q2** Copy this table.

| Number of batteries | Loudness of buzzer | Ammeter reading |
|---|---|---|
| 1 | | |
| 2 | | |

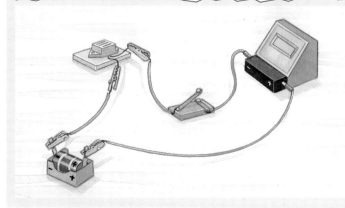

**Q3** What happens to the ammeter reading when you increase the number of batteries in **B**?

**Q4** What happens to the bulb brightness when the electric current is increased?

**Q5** How much electric current flowed through the bulb when it was connected to:
**a** one battery
**b** two batteries
**c** three batteries?

**Q6** In **C**, how did having another bulb in the circuit affect the current?

**Q7** Explain why the ammeter readings in **Q1** and **Q2** are not the same.

**Q8** List the three ways you can change the current in a circuit.

## Using parallel circuits

In this activity you are going to measure current in a parallel circuit.

**Apparatus**
- ammeter ■ wires ■ 2 bulbs
- 2 batteries

**Q1** Copy the table.

| Position of ammeter | Current in amps |
|---|---|
| A1 | |
| A2 | |
| A3 | |

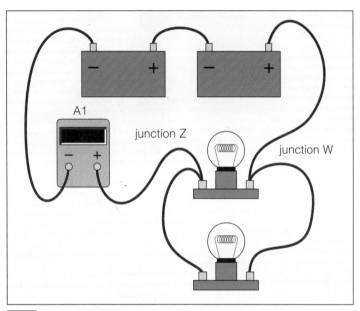

**A** The ammeter measures the current flowing from the battery. Build the circuit. Read the ammeter. Complete the table. Draw the circuit diagram.

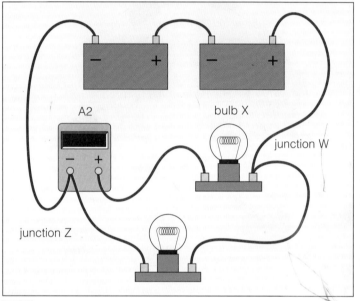

**B** Change the position of the ammeter so that you can measure the current flowing through bulb X. Build the circuit. Read the ammeter. Complete the table. Draw the circuit diagram.

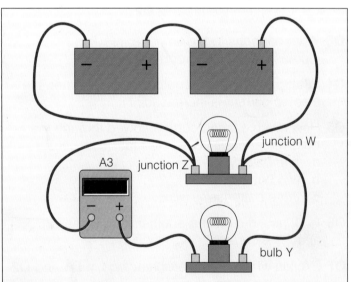

**C** Change the position of the ammeter so that you can measure the current flowing through bulb Y. Build the circuit. Read the ammeter. Complete the table. Draw the circuit diagram.

**Q2** Add the readings of A2 and A3 together.

**Q3** Look at your table. What do you notice about your answer to **Q2**?

**Q4** What do you think happens to the current at junction Z?

**Q5** What do you think happens to the current at junction W?

## Parallel circuits in the home

All the electric circuits in our homes are wired in parallel. Parallel wiring is useful because it means that you can turn lights and other electrical devices on and off without disturbing other lights and devices.

The picture below shows a diagram of the lights and switches on the ground floor of a house. Next to the picture is a plan of this house.

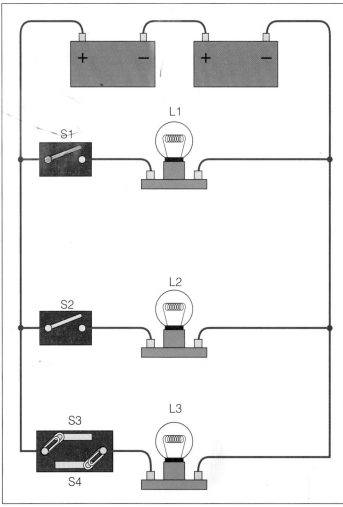

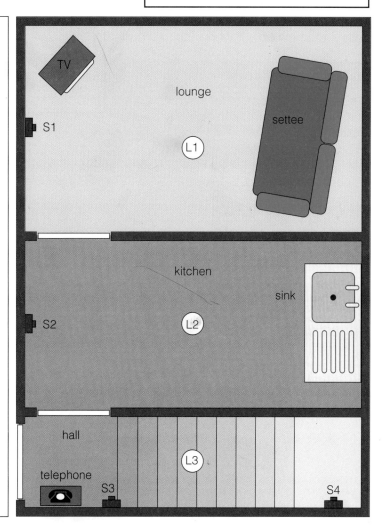

**A** Build the circuit. Use the diagram above to help you make the two-way switch. Draw a circuit diagram in your book.

**B** Switch all the bulbs on. Remove the bulb from the lounge.

**Q1** What happens to the other bulbs when you remove the bulb from the lounge? Explain your answer.

**Q2** Design a table to show which switches control which lights.

**Q3** Why does the bulb on the stairs need a **two-way switch**?

**Q4** Where would you put a safety switch in the circuit to turn all the electricity off?

**Extension exercises 3 and 4 can be used now.**

# 4. An electric hospital trolley

## Make your own trolley

Hospital trolleys are hard to push.

Your school has been asked to make a trolley driven by electricity.
You need to make a model of the trolley, to show how it works.

### Apparatus

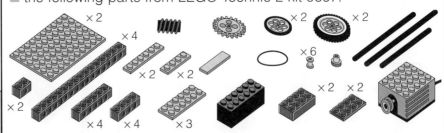

- batteries in battery holder ■ 2 long wires
- the following parts from LEGO Technic 2 kit 9607:

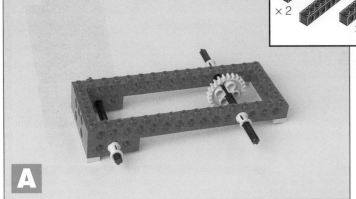

**A**

**B**

**C**

**D**

**E** Using the long wires connect the trolley to the batteries.

**F** Put the trolley on the floor. Switch the electricity on to make sure your trolley works.

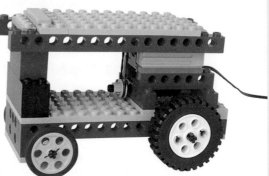

**Q1** Explain how your trolley works. Use these words to help you:

| | |
|---|---|
| batteries | electricity |
| wire | motor |
| belt | wheels |

# Using the trolley

Now you are going to test your trolley.

**Q1** Copy this table.

| Name | Time trolley takes |
|------|--------------------|
|      |                    |

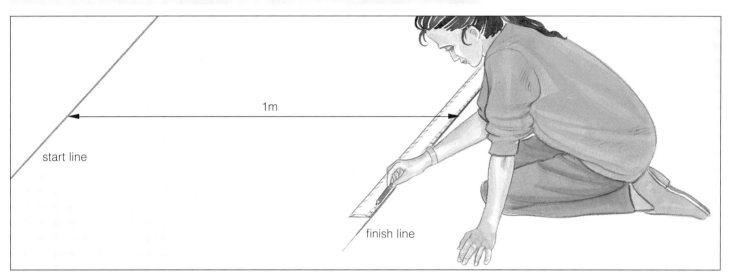

**A** Using the chalk and rule, draw two lines on the floor. The lines must be one metre apart. This is your test track. You are now ready to use your trolley.

**B** Put the trolley 20 cm behind the start line. To switch the motor on connect the battery holder to the trolley.

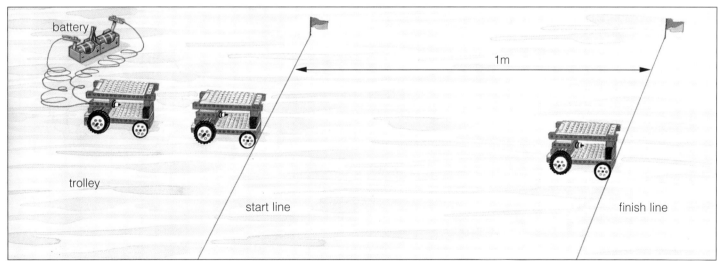

**C** Start the watch when the front wheels of the trolley cross the start line. Stop the watch when the front wheels of the trolley cross the finish line. Complete the table.

**D** Change jobs so that everyone in your group times the trolley.

**Q2** Why are the times different?

**Q3** How can you make sure that the timing of the trolley is a 'fair test'?

Keep your trolley to use later on.

## 4. An electric hospital trolley

## How does the number of batteries affect your trolley?

When your trolley is connected to a battery you have made a series circuit. Adding batteries like this increases the voltage.

In this activity you are going to find out how increasing the number of batteries affects the time your trolley takes to travel one metre.

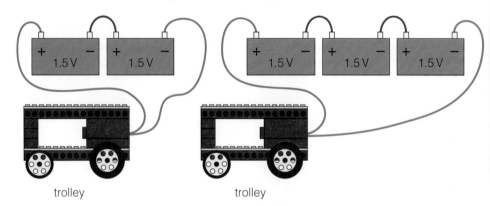

trolley          trolley

### Apparatus

- ■ your trolley ■ 4 batteries ■ wires ■ 2 long wires
- ■ stop watch ■ piece of chalk ■ metre rule
- ■ switch ■ Graph copymaster

**Q1** Copy this table.

| Number of batteries | Time trolley takes (sec.) | | |
|---|---|---|---|
| | Test 1 | Test 2 | Average |
| 2 batteries | | | |
| 3 batteries | | | |
| 4 batteries | | | |

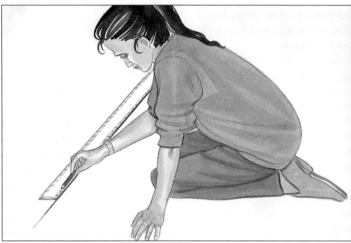

**A** Make a test track for your trolley like the one on page 17.

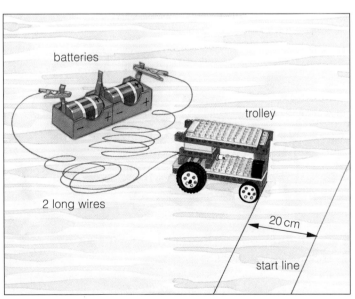

batteries

trolley

2 long wires

20 cm

start line

**B** Put your trolley 20 cm behind the start line. Connect the trolley to two batteries.

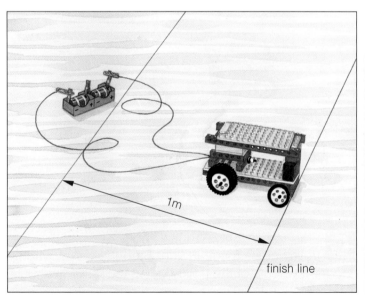

1 m

finish line

**C** When the front wheels of your trolley cross the start line begin timing. When the front wheels of your trolley cross the finish line stop timing. Record the time in the table.

**D** Repeat **B** and **C** once more.

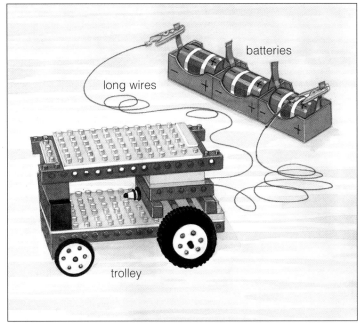

long wires

batteries

trolley

**E** Add another battery to the circuit. Repeat **B** and **C** twice more.

**F** Add another battery to the circuit. Repeat **B** and **C** twice more.

**G** This is how you work out the average time. Use the example to help you. Here are some results.

| Number of batteries | Time trolley takes (sec.) | | |
|---|---|---|---|
| | Test 1 | Test 2 | Average |
| 2 batteries | 4.47 | 4.41 | 4.44 |

Now let's work out the average.

| Test time 1 | + | Test time 2 | = | Total time |
|---|---|---|---|---|
| 4.47 | + | 4.41 | = | 8.88 |

| Total time | ÷ | 2 | = | Average time |
|---|---|---|---|---|
| 8.88 | ÷ | 2 | = | 4.44 |

**Q2** Work out the average time for each number of batteries. Put the averages in the table on page 18.

**Q3** Copy this graph or ask for the Graph copymaster. Fill in your results.

**Q4** How does the number of batteries affect the time your trolley takes to travel one metre?

**Q5** What happens to the speed of the motor when you add more batteries?

**Q6** Does the voltage change when you increase the number of batteries?

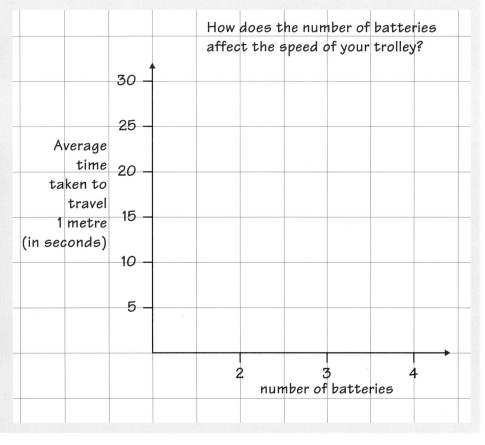

How does the number of batteries affect the speed of your trolley?

Average time taken to travel 1 metre (in seconds)

30
25
20
15
10
5

2    3    4
number of batteries

Keep your trolley to use later on.

# 5. Using a resistor

**Apparatus**

- 1 resistor ■ ammeter
- 2 batteries and holders
- 2 crocodile clips ■ 5 wires
- 2 bulbs and holders ■ motor

## What is resistance?

The hospital has found that the trolleys go too fast. The patients are complaining. One of the hospital engineers thinks a **resistor** in the circuit would help.

Let's see if she is correct.

Resistors are used to control the flow of current in a circuit. Big resistors allow only small currents to flow through them. Small resistors allow large currents to flow through them.

**Q1** Copy the table.

| Components | Reading on ammeter | What happens to component? |
|---|---|---|
| bulb | | |
| bulb and resistor | | |
| motor | | |
| motor and resistor | | |

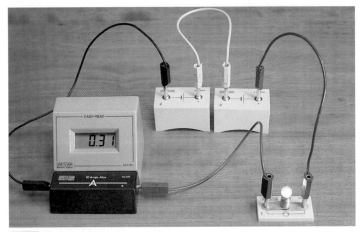

**A** Build the circuit shown in the picture. Record your observations in the table.

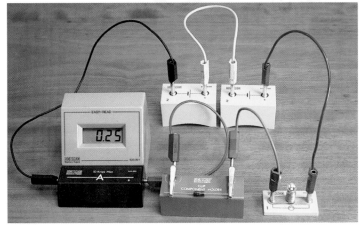

**B** Add a resistor to the circuit. Record your observations in the table.

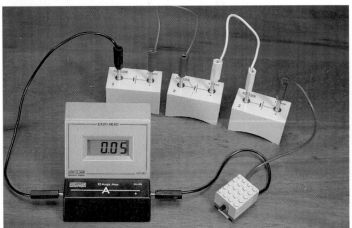

**C** Make the circuit shown in the picture. Record your observations in the table.

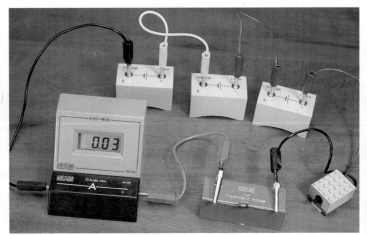

**D** Add a resistor to the circuit. Record your observations in the table.

**Q2** What do resistors do?

**Q3** Why do we have resistors of different sizes?

**Q4** If you put a resistor in series with the motor of your trolley, what will it do?

## Identifying resistors

The school resistors are labelled **A**, **B** and **C**. They look very alike, but their electrical resistances are different. We do not know which is the biggest and which is the smallest. Your task is to sort them in order of size of resistance. To do this you must devise and carry out some experiments.

**A** Work in pairs. Discuss with your partner what you are going to do. Decide what apparatus you will need. Show your plan to your teacher.

**B** Collect your apparatus.

**C** Draw a table to put your results in.

**D** Carry out your experiments.

**E** Write up your experiment. Remember to draw a diagram of your circuit.

# 5. Using a resistor

## Variable resistors

In this activity you are going to make a variable resistor.

In electronics we use variable resistors to control the loudness of buzzers, the speed of motors and the brightness of bulbs. You know that loudness, speed and brightness are controlled by the size of the current flowing through the components. Ask your teacher for the variable resistors copymaster.

### Apparatus

■ 1m length of wire fixed to a metre rule ■ ammeter ■ motor ■ buzzer ■ bulb ■ 2 batteries ■ wires ■ crocodile clip ■ Variable resistors copymaster

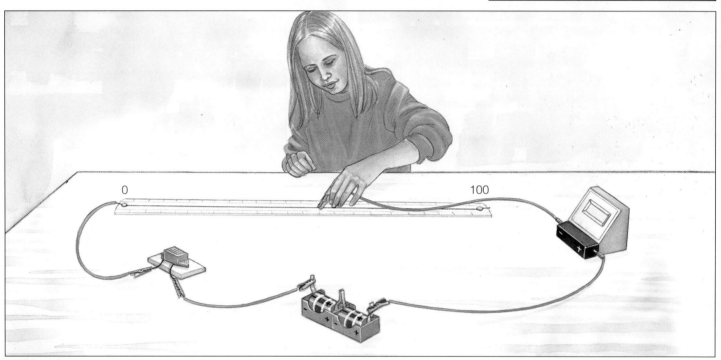

**A** Build this circuit. Slide the crocodile clip along the wire. Notice how the loudness of the buzzer changes. Complete the table on the copymaster.

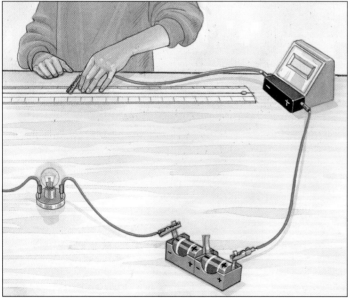

**B** Build this circuit. Slide the crocodile clip along the wire. Notice how the brightness of the bulb changes. Complete the table on the copymaster.

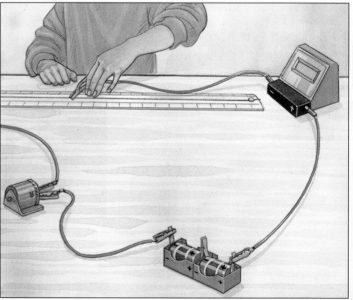

**C** Build this circuit. Slide the crocodile clip along the wire. Notice how the speed of the motor changes. Complete the table on the copymaster.

This is a picture of a variable resistor that you can buy. It has three terminals. When you use it as a variable resistor you use the middle terminal and an end one. Inside is a long piece of wire coiled up to fit into a small space. The resistance is controlled by the spindle which you turn. Turning the spindle changes the length of the wire in the circuit.

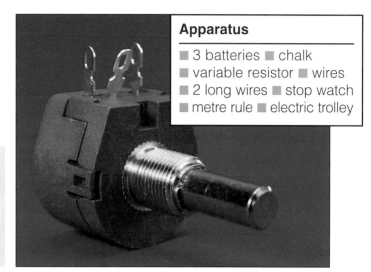

**Apparatus**
- 3 batteries ■ chalk
- variable resistor ■ wires
- 2 long wires ■ stop watch
- metre rule ■ electric trolley

**Q1** Copy this table.

| Resistor setting | Time |
|---|---|
| highest setting | |
| lowest setting | |

**A** Build the circuit.

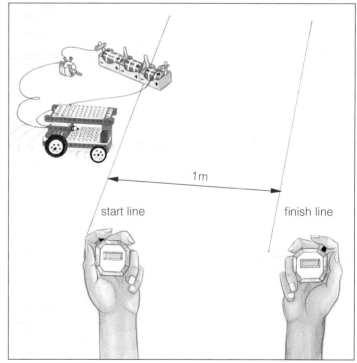

1 m

start line                    finish line

**B** Use a stopwatch to measure the time it takes the trolley to travel one metre at its slowest speed. Complete the table. Repeat this step to measure the time it takes to travel one metre at its fastest speed.

**Q2** Look at your results from the experiment on page 22. What conclusion can you draw about the length of the wire and the current flowing?

**Q3** How does the resistance of the wire change as the length increases?

**Q4** What conclusion can you draw about the resistance of the wire and the current flowing?

**Q5** Give two ways of changing the electric current in a circuit.

**Q6** Work out the **speed** of your trolley when it is going:
  **a** slow
  **b** fast.

$$\text{speed (m/s)} = \frac{\text{total distance travelled (m)}}{\text{total time taken (s)}}$$

**Extension exercise 5 can be used now.**

# 6. Matching card game

## Winner takes all

In this activity you are going to play a card game to help you revise your work. Work in a small group.

**Apparatus**

■ Winner takes all copymaster

**A** Spread the cards face down on the table.

**B** The first player turns over two cards. If the cards match she keeps them and has another go. If the cards do not match she turns them face down again.

**C** Each player takes a turn at matching the cards.

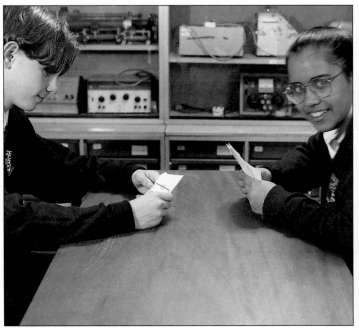

**D** The player with the most cards at the end is the winner.